Hamlet

William Shakespeare

Academic Industries, Inc.
West Haven, Connecticut 06516

ISBN 0-88301-761-X

Published by
Academic Industries, Inc.
The Academic Building
Saw Mill Road
West Haven, Connecticut 06516

Printed in the United States of America

about the author

William Shakespeare was born on April 23, 1564, in Stratford-on-Avon, England, the third child of John Shakespeare, a well-to-do merchant, and Mary Arden, his wife. Young William probably attended the Stratford grammar school, where he learned English, Greek, and a great deal of Latin.

In 1582 Shakespeare married Anne Hathaway. By 1583 the couple had a daughter, Susanna, and two years later the twins, Hamnet and Judith. Somewhere between 1585 and 1592 Shakespeare went to London, where he became first an actor and then a playwright. His acting company, The King's Men, appeared most often in the Globe theatre, a part of which Shakespeare himself owned.

In all, Shakespeare is believed to have written thirty-seven plays, several nondramatic poems, and a number of sonnets. In 1611 when he left the active life of the theatre, he returned to Stratford and became a country gentleman, living in the second-largest house in town. For five years he lived a quiet life. Then, on April 23, 1616, William Shakespeare died and was buried in Trinity Church in Stratford. From his own time to the present, Shakespeare is considered one of the greatest writers of the English-speaking world.

William Shakespeare

Hamlet

Claudius

Gertrude

Ophelia

Hamlet

Horatio

Polonius

Once long ago, King Fortinbras of Norway fought a battle with King Hamlet of Denmark. The winner, they agreed, would become owner of all the other king's riches.

In the battle King Hamlet killed Fortinbras. The dead king's lands were then given to Denmark.

But soon King Hamlet himself died. Many gathered at his funeral.

The king's brother Claudius became the new king. A month later, he married Hamlet's mother.

Then strange things began to happen. At midnight, at the changing of the guard. . . .

I am here to take my turn, Francisco. Has your guard duty been peaceful?

Hello, my friend. Has that *thing* appeared again tonight?

I haven't seen anything.

Horatio doesn't believe us. But if it comes again, he will see it.

It won't appear.

But we've seen it twice!

Last night, just when that star was high . . .

Look! It comes again!

It looks just like the dead king!

But the figure left without saying a word.

No, I saw it too! And it *does* look like the old king. He wore the same armor he fought in against Fortinbras!

I am afraid it is a warning of something bad for our country.

Why do you say that? And why is the country preparing for war?

I'll tell you. You remember that our now-dead king once killed the old king Fortinbras in battle. They had agreed that the winner could take all of the loser's lands.

Now the son, young Fortinbras, has gathered an unlawful army.

They say he means to take back from us the lands his father lost. We must prepare to fight if he attacks us!

And that may be why King Hamlet's ghost has appeared to us!

11

Suddenly the ghost returned. Horatio made up his mind that it would speak to him.

Speak, spirit! If I can help you . . .

or if you can warn us of danger to our country . . .

or if you can tell us of a treasure you once buried, speak!

Suddenly they heard a cock crow. It was dawn.

I'll hit it with my sword!

Stay and speak! Stop it, Marcellus!

It's gone!

The ghost had indeed disappeared, for spirits could not face daylight.

Keep silent about this, both of you! I will tell Prince Hamlet. If the ghost *does* talk, it will be to him.

I know where we can find him.

That morning the court gathered to hear a speech by King Claudius.

Thank you for attending the funeral of my brother, the late king. Thank you, too, for being here when I married my brother's lovely widow.

Such quick action was necessary to keep the country strong.

Then Claudius turned to Laertes, the son of Polonius, the king's advisor.

And now, Laertes. . . .

What can I do for you?

I returned here for King Hamlet's funeral. Now I ask to return to my studies in France.

If your father agrees, you may go.

I do, sir!

Thank you.

Prince Hamlet, son of the dead king, had also returned home from his studies abroad. Claudius turned to him.

And now, Hamlet, what troubles you?

My father's death!

We all must die someday just as your father did! Must you seem so sad?

I *am* sad, Mother. It is deep inside me.

But *all* of us must lose our fathers to death. And someday you will be the king!

Denmark needs you! Please don't ask to leave us!

I will obey you and stay here, Mother.

The court session ended. Everyone left but Hamlet.

He was so good a king, so loving to my mother. . . .

And yet, within a month, she married my uncle!

My heart breaks, but I must keep silent.

Greetings, Prince Hamlet!

Greetings, Horatio! But why are you in Elsinore?

I came home for your father's funeral.

Don't you mean my mother's wedding?

That too, sir. It happened soon afterward. But the good king . . . your father . . . I think I saw him last night!

You *saw* him? Tell me what you mean!

Horatio told Hamlet of the ghost, and how he had tried to make it speak. Greatly excited, Hamlet planned to go and see it for himself.

Meanwhile, Laertes, who had just come from seeing the king, sat and talked with his sister Ophelia.

Before I leave again for France, dear sister, I must warn you . . . Prince Hamlet seems to admire you.

And if it is so?

Stay away from him, Ophelia. He is a prince and he must marry for politics, not love.

I'll remember.

Just then, Polonius arrived to say goodbye.

Farewell, my son! Remember everything I told you!

I will, Father. And Ophelia, remember what I said about Hamlet!

Laertes left, and Polonius turned to his daughter.

Prince Hamlet? I hear you've been spending much time with him!

But, Father, he has spoken to me of love!

He doesn't mean what he says! Do not believe him or see him alone!

I shall obey, Father.

Meanwhile, Hamlet waited anxiously for night, thinking about the ghost. When it was dark, he and his friends met on the castle ramparts.

It is very cold to-night!

What time is it?

It has just struck twelve!

Suddenly the spirit appeared.

Look! It comes!

Hamlet, king, Father . . . speak to me!

It wants you to go away with it!

Don't go!

It may be an evil spirit that will drive you mad!

I am not afraid. I'll follow it!

The ghost led Hamlet to another part of the wall.

Speak, poor ghost!

I am your father's spirit. If ever you loved me . . .

. . . you must kill the evil one who murdered me!

Murdered! Oh, no!

They said I was bitten by a snake as I slept in my orchard. That is not so.

The snake who took my life now wears my crown!

I knew it! My uncle!

19

While I took a nap, my brother poured a deadly poison into my ear!

My life, my crown, my queen were all stolen from me at once!

How horrible!

You must not stand for it! You must get even with him!

Yes! I will!

But don't harm your mother. Her conscience will punish her enough!

There are more things in heaven and earth, Horatio, than you can ever know.

No matter how odd I may seem, don't tell *anyone* about tonight. Now come, let's leave together.

Weeks passed, and Hamlet was becoming very strange. Some said he was mad. Then one day. . . .

Ophelia! What's the matter?

Oh, Father! I was so frightened!

I was sewing. Prince Hamlet rushed into my room.

His clothes were rumpled. His face was as white as his shirt!

He held me by the arm and looked into my eyes for a long time. Then he sighed so sadly!

Perhaps this madness is caused by his love for you!

Have you spoken harshly to him lately?

I have returned his letters and refused to see him as you told me to do!

So I did . . . I had forgotten! Perhaps I was wrong!

We must go the king and tell him of this!

I believe it is caused by his father's death and by our marriage so soon afterward.

Oh, no, Madam! It is his love for my daughter!

In this letter he calls her his most beautiful Ophelia.

He says he cannot write good love poems, but she must believe he loves her anyway.

Hamlet said that to Ophelia?

How did she answer him?

Alas, sir, she did what I told her to do. She refused to see him.

You think this is the trouble.

It could be.

We can find out if it is so. I have a plan.

Sometimes Hamlet walks here alone for hours. I will send Ophelia to him.

Then the king and I will hide behind the curtain. That way, we will learn whether he loves her or not!

We'll try it!

Meanwhile, Rosencrantz and Guildenstern had found Hamlet.

Prince Hamlet!

My dear prince!

My good friends! What brings you to Denmark?

To visit you, dear sir. Nothing else.

Was it your own idea? Weren't you sent for?

What can we say?

If I am your friend, tell me the truth.

My prince, we *were* sent for.

I know, the king and queen called you here. I have lost all pleasure in life. Perhaps I am mad!

No, you're not mad. And something will please you soon, friend. A group of actors is coming here. They are the same ones you saw and enjoyed with us in the city!

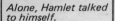
Alone, Hamlet talked to himself.

I have waited and worried. I was afraid to act, afraid I was wrong.

But now I'll have these actors play a murder like my father's!

If my uncle so much as turns pale, I will *know* he is guilty—and then I will kill him!

While Hamlet had been talking to the actors, Polonius and the king carried out their plan with Ophelia.

Walk here, Ophelia, reading this book—and meet Hamlet as if by accident.

Yes, Father.

The king and I will hide here and listen. Quick! Hamlet is coming!

Life is sad. If death is like sleep, it might be better to die.

Ah, the fair Ophelia!

Yes, my prince. I have things you gave me that I wish to return to you.

Not I! I gave you nothing!

You did . . . and beautiful words as well. But words mean nothing when the giver proves unkind.

Ah! Are you honest? Are you beautiful?

I don't know what you mean!

A beautiful woman changes truth to lies! I loved you once.

Indeed, you made me believe so.

You should not have believed me. I love you not! Go enter a nunnery!

Why should you have children who grow up to become sinners?

If you must marry, marry a fool! Wise men know too well what monsters you women make of them with your painted faces, and your sweet talk and acting!

It has driven me mad! I say we must have no more marriages! Go to a nunnery!

After this outburst, Hamlet left the room. The king and Polonius came out from their hiding place.

How sad to see his noble mind so ruined.

It is not love for her that's wrong. Nor is it madness.

There is something in his mind—something he broods over. It could mean danger!

He must be watched! I'll send him to England to collect the money they owe us.

Yes, sir. But first let his mother try to find out his troubles!

She can talk to him after the play! And I will hide myself where I can hear what they are saying.

Very well.

Meanwhile, the time for the play drew near. Hamlet spoke with the leading actor.

Speak these lines as I have told you, neither too strong nor too tame!

Yes, sir.

Then he called Horatio aside.

One scene in the play is like what I believe about my father's death. Watch my uncle! See what he does!

I will, sir.

If he does not show his guilt, then it was a false ghost we saw, and I am wrong.

Here he comes! Find a place.

Oh, no, sir! He has been dead four months!

And still not forgotten?

Then there's hope that a *great* man might be remembered for half a year!

Soon the play began.

Long have we been married and loved each other. Now I am old and ill.

My fear for you is as great as my love!

You see . . . it is a king and queen.

I will die soon, my dear! My hope is that you will find a second husband when I am gone.

I will have no second husband! To love another would be to kill you twice!

You think that now . . . but our feelings change with time.

If, once a widow, I become a wife again, let me be jailed without food or light or hope!

I am tired. Leave me, my dear, and I will nap awhile.

Sweet dreams! And let nothing come between us!

The actor-queen left. Then, as the actor-king slept, another figure crept onto the stage.

This is Lucianus, the nephew of the king.

This poison will quickly end his life!

The nephew poisons him to inherit his riches!

Suddenly there was a disturbance.

You will soon see how the murderer wins the love of the old king's wife!

Look! King Claudius is on his feet!

What? He's frightened!

Stop all this! Give me some light! I must get away!

Stop the play!

The play was ended. Soon everyone had left the hall except Hamlet and Horatio.

I'll take the ghost's word for it, Horatio! Did you see?

I saw very well what happened when there was talk of poisoning!

At this moment Rosencrantz and Guildenstern entered the hall.

Then call his doctor!

Sir, the king is in his room. He is very angry and sick!

Your mother is most worried and sends me to get you.

Of course I will obey my mother!

As Hamlet was about to leave, Polonius walked up to him.

My lord, the queen would speak with you at once!

I will go. You may leave, friends.

Alone, Hamlet talked to himself.

I will go to see her—be cruel—*speak* daggers, but not use them!

Rosencrantz and Guildenstern went immediately to the king.

We will go quickly.

Hamlet is dangerous! I will send him to England with you at once.

Just then Polonius came in.

Hamlet is on his way to his mother. I will hide behind a curtain and listen—and tell you at once what I learn!

Thank you.

After this, Claudius was left alone.

I have murdered my brother! Can I ask heaven to forgive me?

But I want to keep the crown . . . the kingdom . . . the queen. How can I ask to be forgiven?

I can kill him now—while he prays!

That would send his soul to heaven! I want to kill him as he sins, and send him to hell!

Soon Hamlet reached his mother's room.

Mother! Mother!

Tell him you can no longer protect him from the king's anger at his tricks!

Yes. Now hide quickly! Here he comes!

Now, Mother, what's the matter?

Hamlet, you have made your father very angry.

Mother, *you* have made my father very angry.

Don't talk foolishly, Hamlet!

Better foolishly than wickedly as you do, Mother!

My son, have you forgotten who I am?

You are the queen, your husband's brother's wife, and, alas, my mother too.

I must bring someone here who can talk to you!

No, you shall not move!

Not until I show you how you really look—what you really are!

What will you do? Murder me? Help! Help!

Look at my noble father! Hardly was he dead when you married this man, his brother, a murderer!

Oh, Hamlet, stop! You make me think about what I have done, and it disturbs me greatly!

Open your eyes! Look at your husband! He is weak and bad!

Stop! Let me hear no more!

Then we will talk of something else. I am being sent to England with two old friends. They carry sealed orders.

Yes, I had forgotten.

I think they plan trouble for me, but I will turn it around and trouble them. Good night, Mother.

Sadly, the queen went to Claudius and told him of Polonius' death. Not long afterward, Hamlet arrived.

Where is Polonius?

In heaven. Or perhaps the other place!

Hamlet, this deed means that we must send you away quickly—for your own safety!

To England?

Yes. The ship is ready . . . your friends have sealed orders . . . everything is done!

Good! We sail for England!

Rosencrantz and Guildenstern followed Hamlet out. Queen Gertrude returned to her room. Left alone, the king rejoiced.

By my secret orders, the English will put Hamlet to death! Then I will be safe!

And so it happened that as Hamlet went to his ship, he came upon some soldiers.

While all these things were taking place, peace had been made with Norway. Young Fortinbras had agreed not to fight against Denmark. In return, he was allowed to lead his army across Danish territory.

What army is this?

It is led by Fortinbras, nephew of the king of Norway.

He is going to fight against Poland, to win back some land lost by his father.

The land is not worth much. But his fight will be a matter of honor!

This is what a son *should* do, how a son *should* act!

While I think and worry, my father's killer still lives! From now on, my thoughts will be only of revenge.

45

Hamlet sailed for England. But meanwhile, since her father's death, Ophelia had changed. When she spoke, she made no sense. The members of the court were sure she was insane. * One day . . .

Lady Ophelia wishes to see you.

I won't speak with her!

She is half-mad. She speaks of her father.

Tell her to come in.

Ophelia entered with a song.

He is dead and gone, lady,
He is dead and gone;
At his head a grass-green
    turf,
At his heels a stone.

Dear Ophelia!

At this moment the king entered.

Alas! Look here, my king.

How long has she been like this?

I hope all will be well; but I weep to think they put him in the cold ground. I must tell my brother!

I thank you. Come, get me my coach! Good night, ladies. Good night, sweet ladies!

Follow her, and watch her closely.

Yes, sir.

Alone with the queen, Claudius spoke.

We have so many troubles, Gertrude! Ophelia's father killed . . . your son to blame . . . people are whispering bad things!

47

Laertes has returned secretly from France! He is listening to gossip about his father's death.

Suddenly . . .

Save yourself, sir! Laertes at the head of a mob has overpowered your guards!

Laertes shall be king! We choose Laertes!

Evil king, where is my father?

Dead.

But the king did not kill him! Be calm, Laertes!

At this moment Ophelia appeared.

Dear sister, sweet Ophelia!

Here's some rosemary. That's to make you remember.

48

There's a daisy. I would give you violets, but they all withered when my father died.

Do you see this? I *will* have revenge!

I grieve for your father, too. And you *shall* have revenge.

Come with me. Listen to my story. You will hear whose fault it is.

Very well. I will listen.

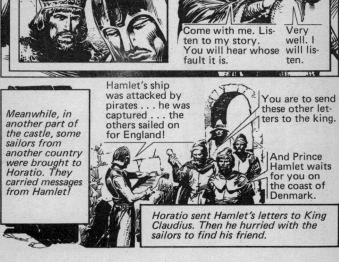

Meanwhile, in another part of the castle, some sailors from another country were brought to Horatio. They carried messages from Hamlet!

Hamlet's ship was attacked by pirates . . . he was captured . . . the others sailed on for England!

You are to send these other letters to the king.

And Prince Hamlet waits for you on the coast of Denmark.

Horatio sent Hamlet's letters to King Claudius. Then he hurried with the sailors to find his friend.

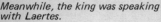

Meanwhile, the king was speaking with Laertes.

. . . so you see, it was Hamlet who killed your father . . . and he thought he was killing *me*!

But why haven't you pun- ished him?

His mother loves him very much, and I love her! The people love him too. But I shall tell you more later, and I think you will be satisfied.

As Claudius said this, a messenger entered, bringing Hamlet's letters.

The letters say that Hamlet is still alive! He is in Denmark and asks me to see him!

Then I will accuse him of my father's murder face to face!

I have a plan! He will die . . . and not even his mother can blame me for it!

As long as I may be the one to do it!

We have heard reports that in France you became an expert swordsman.

And what of that?

When Hamlet heard it, he wanted to try his skill against yours. We'll arrange a practice match.

Yes.

The practice swords will not be sharp. But Hamlet is so honest and trusting that he will not look closely. You will pick a sharp sword—and use it!

I'll do it!

And I'll put poison on my sword! Even a scratch from it will kill him!

Good! And just to be *sure* he dies. . . .

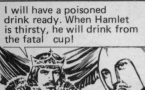

I will have a poisoned drink ready. When Hamlet is thirsty, he will drink from the fatal cup!

Wait! Who's there?

One dreadful thing after another! Your sister, Laertes . . . she is drowned!

What? Drowned! Where?

She took some flowers to a spot where a willow branch slants across a stream.

She climbed the branch to hang her flowers on it. The branch broke!

My poor Ophelia!

She floated for a while, singing songs. And then she sank.

I must leave! I will weep for her in private!

We must follow him. Who knows what he will do now?

While Queen Gertrude had been explaining Ophelia's death, Horatio had gone to meet Hamlet on the beach. As they returned together they came to a churchyard.

Whose grave are you digging?

One that was a woman, sir; but, rest her soul, she's dead!

Look! The king, the queen! Whose body do they bury? Let us hide and watch!

Farewell! I had hoped to scatter flowers at your wedding to Hamlet, not on your grave!

They're burying Ophelia!

Why do you treat me so? I've always liked you, Laertes!

He is mad!

A fit will come on him sometimes, but afterward he is as gentle as a dove.

None of this matters anyway. Come, Horatio.

Be calm, Laertes. Our plan will work out.

Back at the castle, Hamlet told Horatio what had happened to him.

Secretly I read the sealed orders carried by Guildenstern and Rosencrantz.

King Claudius commanded the English to cut off my head!

What?

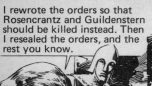

I rewrote the orders so that Rosencrantz and Guildenstern should be killed instead. Then I resealed the orders, and the rest you know.

Yes, It was in your letter . . . the pirates, the sea-fight, and your escape!

Just then, a servant entered.

My prince, I have a message from the king.

Tell me what it is.

Laertes is said to be a most skillful fighter with the sword.

I know.

But the king thinks you are just as skillful, and he has made a bet.

Six fine horses against six French daggers, that you can fight as well as Laertes does.

I will fight him here.

I will tell the king.

Within a few minutes the members of the court had arrived to see the practice match.

Come, Hamlet, and take Laertes' hand.

I ask your pardon, Laertes. If I have wronged you, I never meant to do it!

I will forgive you when my honor is satisfied.

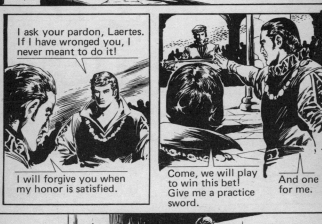

Come, we will play to win this bet! Give me a practice sword.

And one for me.

This will do. They are all the same length?

Yes, sir.

This is too heavy. Give me another.

Suddenly Laertes lunged and wounded Hamlet with his sharp sword.

I'll hit him now!

At once Hamlet knocked Laertes' sword from his hand. Each fighter picked up the other's sword . . . and they fought on.

Both men are bleeding! How is that?

The queen faints at the sight of blood!

No, no! The drink, Hamlet! I am poisoned!

And I will die . . . hit with my own sword!

Lock the doors! We'll find out what is happening here!

This sword is poisoned, Hamlet. You will be dead in half an hour, and I as well. Your mother's poisoned. The king, the king's to blame!

This is a poisoned sword? Then I must use it!

Help! Help!

And here, you murderer! Drink this! Follow my mother!

I will drink and die with you!

No, Horatio. If you are my friend, stay alive and tell this story!

Suddenly from outside there were drumbeats and shots.

What warlike noise is that?

Young Fortinbras has come with his army from Poland!

I'm dying, Horatio. Fortinbras has my vote to become king of Denmark.

His noble heart has stopped. Good night, sweet prince! May flights of angels sing you to your rest!

Fortinbras entered the hall.

So many princes dead? So many bodies? What does this mean?

Put the bodies high on a stage, and I will tell the world how these things happened. The bloody acts, the wrong judgments, the mistaken purposes. . . .

Take up the bodies.

Let four captains carry Hamlet. Had he lived, he would have been a great king!

THE END

COMPLETE LIST OF POCKET CLASSICS AVAILABLE

CLASSICS

C 1 Black Beauty
C 2 The Call of the Wild
C 3 Dr. Jekyll and Mr. Hyde
C 4 Dracula
C 5 Frankenstein
C 6 Huckleberry Finn
C 7 Moby Dick
C 8 The Red Badge of Courage
C 9 The Time Machine
C10 Tom Sawyer
C11 Treasure Island
C12 20,000 Leagues Under the Sea
C13 The Great Adventures of Sherlock Holmes
C14 Gulliver's Travels
C15 The Hunchback of Notre Dame
C16 The Invisible Man
C17 Journey to the Center of the Earth
C18 Kidnapped
C19 The Mysterious Island
C20 The Scarlet Letter
C21 The Story of My Life
C22 A Tale of Two Cities
C23 The Three Musketeers
C24 The War of the Worlds
C25 Around the World in Eighty Days
C26 Captains Courageous
C27 A Connecticut Yankee in King Arthur's Court
C28 The Hound of the Baskervilles
C29 The House of the Seven Gables
C30 Jane Eyre
C31 The Last of the Mohicans
C32 The Best of O. Henry
C33 The Best of Poe
C34 Two Years Before the Mast
C35 White Fang
C36 Wuthering Heights
C37 Ben Hur
C38 A Christmas Carol
C39 The Food of the Gods
C40 Ivanhoe
C41 The Man in the Iron Mask
C42 The Prince and the Pauper
C43 The Prisoner of Zenda
C44 The Return of the Native
C45 Robinson Crusoe
C46 The Scarlet Pimpernel

COMPLETE LIST OF POCKET CLASSICS AVAILABLE
(cont'd)

C47 The Sea Wolf
C48 The Swiss Family Robinson
C49 Billy Budd
C50 Crime and Punishment
C51 Don Quixote
C52 Great Expectations
C53 Heidi
C54 The Illiad
C55 Lord Jim
C56 The Mutiny on Board H.M.S. Bounty
C57 The Odyssey
C58 Oliver Twist
C59 Pride and Prejudice
C60 The Turn of the Screw

SHAKESPEARE

S 1 As You Like It
S 2 Hamlet
S 3 Julius Caesar
S 4 King Lear
S 5 Macbeth
S 6 The Merchant of Venice
S 7 A Midsummer Night's Dream
S 8 Othello
S 9 Romeo and Juliet
S10 The Taming of the Shrew
S11 The Tempest
S12 Twelfth Night